HAMPSHIRE COUNTY LIBRARY
WITHDRAWN.

A SELECTION FROM THE

PASSION OF OUR LORD

ACCORDING TO ST. JOHN

Composed by

G. F. HANDEL

Edited by

J. MICHAEL DIACK

Foreword by

Sir WALFORD DAVIES

(Full Score and String parts on hire)

Paterson's Publications Ltd.

Printed in Great Britain

FOREWORD

BY

SIR WALFORD DAVIES

IT is a pleasure to be allowed to welcome with a word of appreciation and thanks the effort of Mr. J. Michael Diack to make Handel's short St. John Passion available to-day for ordinary use in Churches and Chapels and by Choral Societies in this country. His task of adaptation and of editing the work for homely and devotional purposes has been a delicate and difficult one. But it seems to me to have been undertaken with befitting reverence and discernment. No one must seek here for a literal text of the original work; that they will find in the Chrysander edition, printed for the German Handel Society (and published by Breitkopf and Hartel), to which edition Mr. Diack has himself gone on our behalf. If this work has to be used in Christian places of worship to-day, it is obviously necessary that the many reiterations of the text of the Passion story in Handel's original setting should be drastically but devoutly curtailed. The English Scriptural text is clearly of more commanding importance to worshippers than the exact musical text written for German words. Not only so, but when Handel, in his original, repeats the words of Christ, "Women, behold thy Son" (spoken as they were on the Cross) three times, in Arioso style, it should be remembered by all of us (as by the Editor) that the eighteenth century was but four years old and the composer himself nineteen. It is hard to believe that Handel would have done this when in the inspired mind which penned the notes to "He looked for some to have pity on Him" in the Messiah. In place after place where the repetitions do not seem to inflict any vital hurt upon the spirit of the text, as we in England use and understand it, the Editor has preserved them here. But in such vital instances as that named above, he has not only cut out the repetitions but changed the notes themselves so that while preserving the spirit and manner of Handel they shall yet do no violence to the English Scriptural text. If he had done this badly,—if he had shown even the mildest editorial arrogance or complacency or ignorance, one must suppose that no amount of well-meaning on his part would save it from blame and oblivion. But if, as I believe, he has done it reverently, musically, and in a way consistent with Handel's style and intentions, he will not only earn our gratitude but will have supplied many village choirs in the country with a practical and beautiful stepping-stone to the far more difficult St. Matthew and St. John Passions of Bach.

It would seem that the whole work should be sung more meditatively than dramatically, and that at every point it should be undertaken and thought of never as a performance but rather as an act of devotion by all taking part. It is good to remember that meditative repetitions can seem fitting when all other kinds of repetitions are vain.

Walford Davies.

April, 1932.

In addition to the "curtailments" referred to by Sir Walford Davies in his foreword, the following numbers in the German Handel Society's edition have been omitted from this the first English edition :—

No. 12	Soprano	Air	"Oh, Son of God."
No. 16	Bass	Air	"Loud thundering" (first part).
No. 23	Tenor	Air	"The coat that Thou didst lose."
No. 24	Quartetto	—	"Let us not rend it."
No. 32	Soprano	Air	"Tremble, ye mountains."
No. 33	Evangelist	—	"The Jews therefore."
No. 34	Soprano and Bass	Duet	"Can the sin be washed away."
No. 35	Evangelist	—	"And he that saw it."
No. 36	Soprano and Bass	Duet	"I'll follow to the tomb."

The added chorales, Nos. 13a, 20a, and 31a, are from another Passion by Handel.

The chorus, "Behold the Lamb of God," from "The Messiah," is suggested as an opening number, and the first three bars of the same chorus may be used as a prelude to No. 31.

J. M. D.

Soloists.

EVANGELIST *Tenor.*		TWO SOPRANOS.
PILATE *Baritone.*		ALTO.
JESUS *Bass.*		BASS.

Index.

If preferred, the hymns "When I survey" *(Tune,"Rockingham") and* "O Sacred Head" ***may be*** *sung in place of Nos 13ª and 20ª*

Time of performance one hour.

Orchestral accompaniment of strings

Opening Chorus.-"Behold the Lamb of God."

From The Messiah.

way, tak-eth a-way the sin of the world;
way the sin of the world; Be-
pp
tak - eth a-way the sin of the world; Be-
tak - eth a-way the sin of the world;
Be-hold the Lamb of God, the Lamb of God, of
hold the Lamb of God, the Lamb of God, Be-hold the Lamb of
hold the Lamb of God. Be - hold the Lamb of God, Be
Be-hold the Lamb of
p
God, the Lamb of God, that tak - eth a-way the
God, the Lamb of God, that tak - eth a-way the
hold the Lamb of God, that tak - eth a-way the
God, that tak - eth a-way the

sin of the world, of the world; Be-hold the Lamb of God, be-
sin of the world, the sin of the world; Be-hold the Lamb of God, the
sin of the world, the sin of the world; Be-hold the Lamb of God, the
sin of the world, the sin of the world; Be-hold the Lamb of God, the
hold the Lamb of God, that tak-eth a-way the sin of the world,
Lamb of God, that tak-eth a-way the sin, the
Lamb of God, that tak-eth a-way the
Lamb of God, that tak-eth a-way the
that tak-eth a-way
sin of the world, the sin of the world, that
sin of the world, the sin of the world,
sin of the world, the sin of the world,

the sin of the world,
tak - eth a-way the sin, the sin of the world, the sin of the
that tak - eth a - way the sin of the world, the sin of the
that tak - eth a - way the sin of the world, the sin of the
dim.
pp
the sin of the world, that tak eth a - way the sin of the
world, the sin of the world, that tak-eth a - way the sin of the
pp
world, the sin of the world, that tak-eth a - way the sin of the
world, that tak-eth a - way the sin of the
pp
pp
world.
world.
world.
world.

The Passion.

according to Saint John.

3. Chorus. "Hail! King of Judah!"

hail, all hail to Thee — King of Ju - - dah!
hail, all hail to Thee — King of Ju - - dah!
hail, all hail to Thee — King of Ju - - dah!
hail, all hail to Thee — King of Ju - - dah!
King of Ju-dah, hail, all hail to Thee,
King of Ju-dah, hail, all hail to Thee,
King of Ju-dah, hail, all hail to Thee,
King of Ju-dah, hail, all hail to Thee,
hail — King of Ju - dah!
hail — King of Ju - dah!
hail King of Ju - dah!
hail — King of Ju - dah!

4. Recit. "And they smote Him."

5. Duet. "Now is our Saviour."

Yet He is love-li - er far than the blos - soms
Yet He is love-li - er far than the blos - soms
p

Which the fair mea-dows, which the fair mea-dows of Ju - dah a - dorn,
Which the fair mea-dows fair mea-dows of Ju - dah a - dorn,

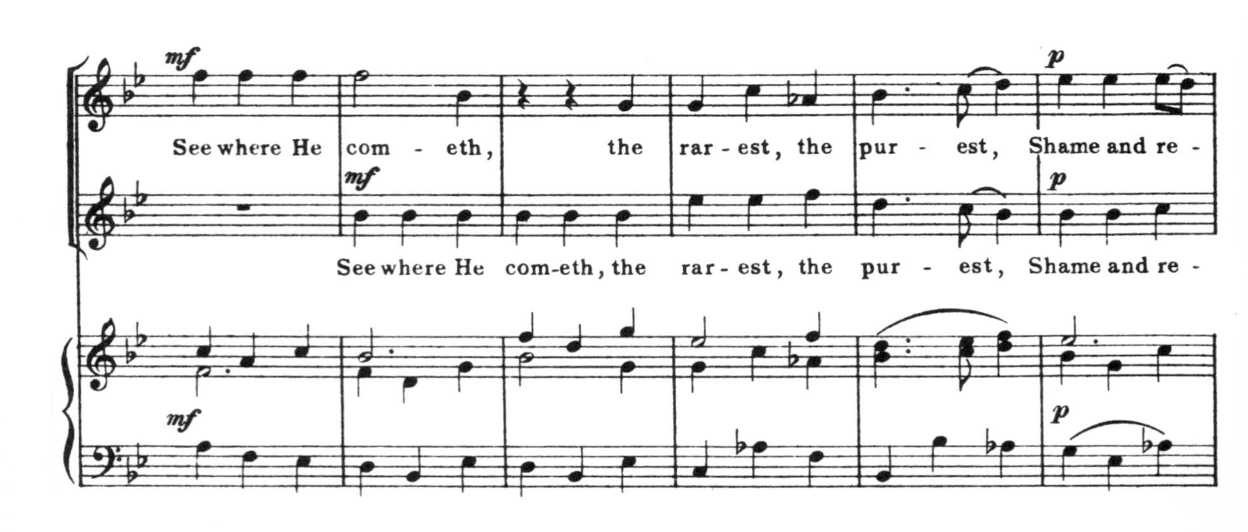
mf
See where He com - eth, the rar - est, the pur - est, Shame and re -
p
mf
See where He com-eth, the rar - est, the pur - est, Shame and re -
p
mf
p

-vil-ing He meek-ly en - dur - est, See where He com-eth, the rar-est, the
-vil-ing He meek-ly en - dur - est, See where He com-eth, the rar-est, the
pp
pur - est, See where He com-eth, the rar - est, the pur - est, Shame and re -
pur - est, See where He com-eth, the rar - est, the pur - est, Shame and re -
-vil - ing He meek - ly en - dur - est.
-vil - ing He meek - ly en - dur - est.
p
pp

6. Recit. "Pilate saith unto them."

7. Chorus. "Crucify!"

8. Recit. "Then Pilate saith unto them."

9. Chorus. "We have a sacred law."

God, for He made Himself, He made Him-self the Son of God,
mf for He made Himself, cresc. for He made Him-self the Son of God.
for He made Himself, for He made Himself the Son of God.
mf for He made Him-self, cresc. for He made Him-self the Son of God.
for He made Him-self, for He made Him-self the Son of God.

10. Recit. "When Pilate heard that saying."

I have pow'r, know'st Thou not that I have pow'r,
pow'r to cru - - - - - ci - fy Thee,
mp
and have al - so pow'r, and have al - so pow'r, have pow'r to re -
lease Thee, to re - lease Thee, to re - lease Thee and I have
p
EVANGELIST
pow'r, have pow'r to release Thee?
Je - sus answered
mf

11. Arioso. "Thou couldst have no pow'r."

— the great - - er, the great-er sin, there-fore
he that de - liv-er'd Me un - to thee, hath the great - er
sin, he hath the great - er sin.
p
mf
mp
pp
→p 27

12. Recit. "And from thenceforth".

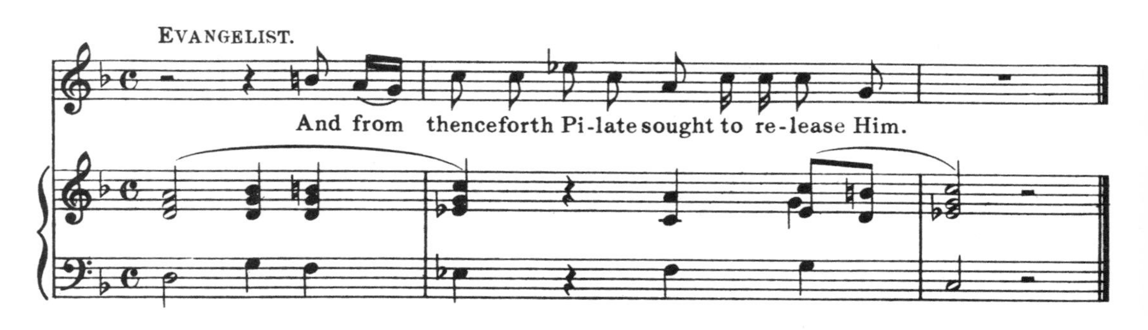

13. Solo. "Sins of ours of deepest stain".

For our sins, for our sins
He was des-pis-ed, He was despis-ed, Son of God, by man chastis-ed,
Son of God, by man chas-tis - ed. For our
sins He was des-pis-ed, Son of God, by man chastis-ed, Son of God, by man chastis -
- ed.
p
cresc.
mp
dim.
f

13a. Chorale. "Although our sin is great indeed."

14. Recit. "But the Jews cried out."

Chorus. "If thou let this man go."

if thou let this man go, thou art not a
if thou let this man go, this man go, if thou let this man
if thou let this man go, thou art not a friend of Cae-sar,
if thou let this man, if thou let this man go, thou art not a friend of Cae-sar,
friend of Cae-sar, if thou let this man go, this man go,
go, thou art not a friend of Cae-sar, if thou let this man go, this man
thou art not, thou art not a friend of Cae-sar, if thou let this man
thou art not, thou art not a friend of Cae-sar,
if thou let this man go, thou, thou art not a friend of Cae -
go, this man go, thou art not, thou art not, thou art not a friend of Cae -
go, this man go, thou art not, thou art not, thou art not a friend of Cae -
if thou let this man go, thou art not, thou art not, thou art not a friend of Cae -

-sar;
-sar;
-sar;
-sar;
mf
whoso-ev-er maketh him - self a king,
mf
whoso-ev-er maketh him - self a
mf
mf
who - so - ev - er mak - eth him - self a king,
who - so - ev - er mak - eth him - self a
king, who - so - ev - er
who - so - ev - er mak - eth him -
cresc.
who - so - ev - er mak - eth him - self a king,
king, who - so - ev - er mak - eth him -
cresc.
mak - eth him - self a king, mak - eth him -
cresc.
-self a king, who - so - ev - er
cresc.

speak-eth, speak-eth a - gainst Cae - sar,
- self a king, speaketh a - gainst Cae - sar,
- self a king, speak - eth a - gainst Cae - sar,
mak-eth him - self a king, speaketh a - gainst Cae - sar,
f
who-so-ev-er maketh him-self a king, speaketh a - gainst Cae -
who-so-ev-er maketh him-self a king, speaketh a - gainst Cae -
who-so-ev-er maketh him-self a king, speaketh a - gainst Cae -
who-so-ev-er maketh him-self a king, speaketh a - gainst Cae -
- sar, speak-eth a - gainst Cae - sar.
- sar, speak-eth a - gainst Cae - sar.
- sar, speak-eth a - gainst Cae - sar.
- sar, speak-eth a - gainst Cae - sar.

15. Recit. "When Pilate heard that saying."

16. Chorus. "Away with Him."

Presto.
A-way with Him, a-way with Him, a-
A-way with Him, a-way with Him, a-way with Him,
A-way with Him, a-way with Him, a-way, a-way with
A-way with Him, a-way with Him,
Presto.
Adagio.
-way with Him, a-way, a-way! Cru-ci-fy Him!
a-way with Him, a-way, a-way! Cru-ci-fy Him!
Him, a-way, a-way! Cru-ci-fy Him!
a-way with Him, a-way, a-way! Cru-ci-fy Him!
Adagio.

17. Arioso "Consider ye."

Bass.

— can Sa-tan's power o'er Him pre-vail? Con-si-der ye,
con-si-der ye, who, God de-fy-ing, His well-loved Son are cru-ci-
fy-ing, Can Sa-tan's power o'er Him prevail, can Sa-tan's power o'er Him pre-
vail, can Sa-tan's power, can Sa-tan's power o'er Him prevail?
mf
f
mp
p

18. Recit "Pilate saith unto them."

king but Cae - sar,
we have no king but
Cae - sar,
no
king but Cae - sar,
have no king
but
Cae - sar,
we have no king, we
We have no king, we
have no king
but
Cae sar,
we have no king but
Cae - sar,
no
king
but
we
have no king, we
have
no
king
but
have no king but Cae - sar,
we
have
no king, we
Cae - sar,
we
have no king, we
f
Cae - sar,
we have no king but
Cae - sar,
we
have no king, we
have no king
but
have no king
but
Cae - sar
we
have no king
but
Cae - sar,

cresc. e accel.
Cae - sar, no king but Cae - sar, we have no king, we
cresc. e accel.
Cae - sar, we have no king, we
cresc. e accel.
have no king, we have no king but Cae - sar, we have no king, we
we have no king but Cae sar, we have no king, we
cresc. e accel.
have no king but Cae-sar, no king but Cae-sar, we have no king but
have no king but Cae-sar, no king but Cae-sar, we have no king but
have no king but Cae-sar, no king but Cae-sar, we have no king but
have no king but Cae-sar. no king but Cae-sar. we have no king but
Cae - sar, have no king, no king but Cae - sar!
Cae - sar, have no king, no king but Cae - sar!
Cae - sar, have no king, no king but Cae - sar!
Cae - sar, have no king, no king but Cae - sar!

20. Recit. "Then delivered he Him unto them."

20 a. Chorale. "O Love of God."

F. W. FABER.

21. Solo. "Take courage, soul."

Alto.

mf
He is the Rock, He is the Rock 'gainst
p
mf
which no power pre-vail - - - - - - - - - eth,
f
He is the Rock 'gainst which no power pre-vail-eth, Our strong de-
f
fence, when Sa - tan's power as-sail - - - eth. Fear not, His
power thou soon shalt see, fear not, His power thou soon shalt

22. Recit. "And Pilate wrote a title."

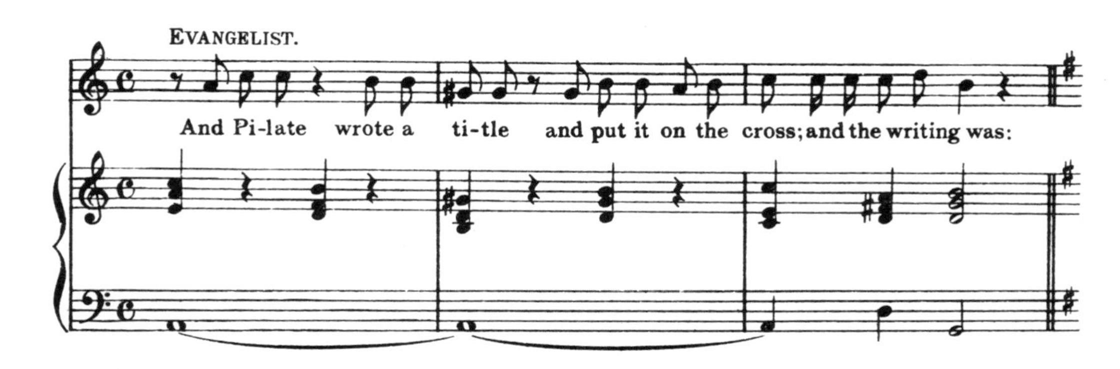

Adagio.
Je - sus of Na - za-reth,
Je - sus of Na - za-reth,
mf
the king of the Jews.
This title read many of the
p
Adagio.
Jews, for the place was nigh to the cit - y where Je - sus was—
cru - ci - fied; and it was writ - ten in He - brew, and Greek,
and La-tin. Then said the chief priests of the Jews un-to Pi - late.

23. Chorus "Write not, the king of the Jews."

said: I am king, but that He said, I am king, that He said, I am king, the
but that He said I am king, He said, I am king, that He said, I am king, the
of the Jews, that He said I am king, but that He said, that He said, I am king, the
king of the Jews, that He said, I am king, I am king of the Jews, that He said, I am king, the
king of the Jews, I am the king of the Jews.
king of the Jews, I am the king of the Jews.
king of the Jews, I am the king of the Jews.
king — of the Jews, I am the king of the Jews.

24. Recit "Pilate answered."

eve - ry sold - ier a part;
and al - so His coat.
Adagio.
That the Scrip-ture might be ful - fill - ed, which saith:
"They part - ed my
p
rai - ment a - mong them, and for my vest - ure they did cast
lots."
These things therefore the soldiers did.

25. Duet "By the Cross of Jesus standing."*

Soprano and Alto.

* *From a hymn by Horatius Bonar.*

straitened souls ex-pand-ing,
As we gaze up-on His
pand-ing, love our straitened souls ex - panding,
As we
mf
p
face. Health from yonder Tree is
flow - - - ing, health from yonder Tree is flow -
gaze up-on His face. Health from yonder Tree is
flow - - - ing, health from yonder Tree is
ing,
A heavenly
light,
a heaven-ly
flow - - - - ing,
A heavenly light,
mp

light is on it glow - ing, on it glow - ing, A heavenly
a heavenly light, a heaven - ly light, a light is on it glow-ing, a
p
light, a heavenly light is on it glow - ing, a heavenly light, a heavenly light is on it
light, a heavenly light, a heavenly light is on it glowing, a light, a heavenly light is on it
glow - ing.
glow - ing.
mf

26. Recit. "Now there stood by the Cross."

JESUS.
EVANGELIST.
Wo-man, be-hold thy son! Then saith He to the dis-ci-ple:
Adagio.
p
JESUS.
Son! be - hold, be-hold thy moth - - er!
Adagio.
EVANGELIST.
And from that hour that dis-ci-ple took her to his own home. Af-ter this Je-sus know-ing that
all things were now accomplished, that the Scrip-ture might be ful - fill-ed, saith:
Adagio.
JESUS.
I thirst!

27. Solo "Jesus, wherefore thirsteth Thou."

Soprano.

pp
Dear-est Lord! Didst Thou cry in bit - ter pain, bit - ter
pp
p
pain, Thirst - ing for the souls of men, thirst-ing for
the souls of men? Didst Thou cry in bit - ter pain,
pp
bit - ter pain, Thirst - ing for the souls of men,
thirst-ing for the souls of men?

28. Recit. "Now there was set a vessel."

⊕ *A cut is suggested to* ⊕

29. Solo. "Oh work sublime."

Bass.

⊕ *If the cut is made to* ⊕ *the solo part in the preceeding bar will be silent.*

30. Recit. "And He bowed His head."

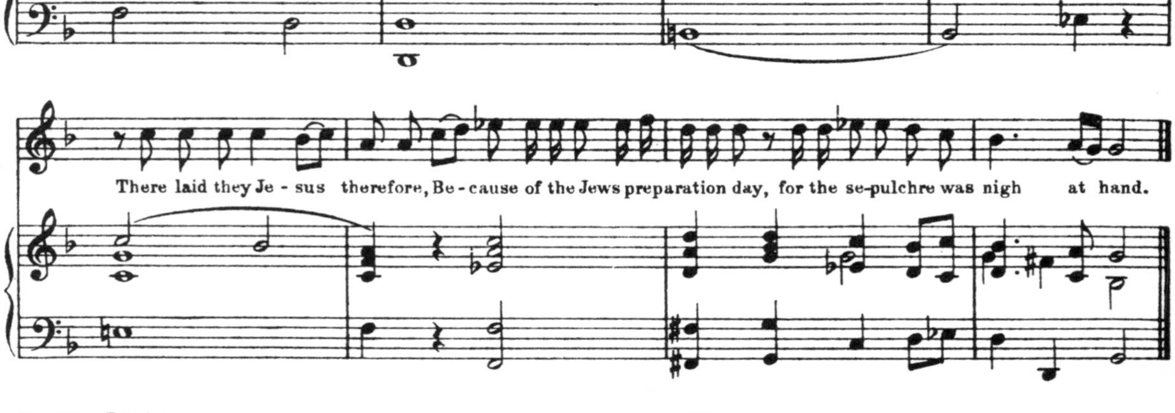

31. Chorus. "Sweetly sleep."

(*The first three bars of* "Behold the Lamb of God" *may be used as a prelude.*)

work is done!
sweetly sleep,
work is done!
sweetly
work is done!
sweetly
work is done!
sweetly
mp
Thy warfare o - ver! soft - ly
sleep, sweetly sleep, Thy war - fare o - ver! soft - ly rest,
sleep, sweetly sleep, Thy war - fare o - ver! soft - ly
sleep, sweetly sleep, Thy war - fare o - ver! soft - ly
rest soft - ly rest, soft - ly rest, Thy work is done!
soft - ly rest, Thy work is done!
rest soft - ly rest, soft - ly rest, Thy work is done!
rest soft - ly rest, soft - ly rest, Thy work is done!
mf

Now can death no longer
Now can death no longer
Now can death no longer
Now can death no longer
p
mf
sev - er, Thou hast vanquished death for
ev - er, Fought the fight, the vic - t'ry
sev - er, Thou hast vanquished death for
ev - er, Fought the fight, the vic - t'ry
sev - er, Thou hast vanquished death for
ev - er, Fought the fight, the vic - t'ry
sev - er, Thou hast vanquished death for
ev - er, Fought the fight, the vic - t'ry
cresc.
f
won.
Thou hast vanquishd death for
ev - er, Fought the fight the vic-t'ry
won.
Thou hast vanquishd death for
ev - er, Fought the fight the vic-t'ry
won.
Thou hast vanquishd death for
ev - er, Fought the fight the vic-t'ry
won.
Thou hast vanquishd death for
ev - er, Fought the fight the vic-t'ry
f
cresc.

won, fought the fight, fought the fight,
won, fought the fight, fought the fight,
won, fought the fight, fought the
won, fought the fight, fought the fight, fought the
f
fought the fight, the vic - t'ry won.
fought the fight, the vic - t'ry won.
fight, the vic - t'ry won.
fight, the vic - t'ry won.
p
Sweetly sleep,
p
Sweetly
p
Sweetly
p
Sweetly
p

Thy war-fare o - - ver! Soft-ly rest, soft-ly
sleep, sweetly sleep, Thy war-fare o - ver! Softly rest,
sleep, sweetly sleep, Thy war-fare o - ver! soft-ly rest, soft-ly
sleep, sweetly sleep, Thy war-fare o - ver! soft-ly rest, soft-ly
rest, softly rest, Thy work is done!
softly rest, softly rest, Thy work is done!
rest, softly rest, softly rest, Thy work is done!
rest, softly rest, softly rest, Thy work is done!
sweet-ly sleep, sweet-ly sleep, Thy
sweet-ly sleep, sweet-ly sleep, Thy
sweet-ly sleep, Thy
sweet-ly sleep, sweet-ly sleep, Thy
p

war - fare o - ver!
soft-ly rest, soft-ly rest, soft-ly
war - fare o - ver!
soft-ly rest,
soft-ly
war - fare o - ver!
soft-ly rest, soft-ly rest, soft-ly
war - fare o - ver!
soft-ly rest, soft-ly rest, soft-ly
rest, Thy work is done!
rest, Thy work is done!
rest, Thy work is done!
rest, Thy work is done!
pp

31ª Chorale. "Soul, array thyself with gladness."

CATHERINE WINKWORTH.

Schmücke dich
arranged by
G. F. HANDEL.

-ness,
Come in-to the
day-light's splen
dour,
There with joy thy
prais-es ren
der.
Un-to Him whose
grace un-bound
ed
Hath this won-drous
p
f
mp

Reproduced and printed by
Halstan & Co. Ltd., Amersham, Bucks.

A SELECTION FROM THE

PASSION OF OUR LORD

ACCORDING TO ST. LUKE

Attributed to

J. S. BACH

Arranged by
REV. A. HASTINGS KELK, M.A.
and
J. MICHAEL DIACK

PATERSON'S PUBLICATIONS LTD